CW00348588

Disney · PIXAR

This Annual belongs to

....

Age ....

Disney

ANNUAL 2011

Welcome to...

... the Disney Pixar Annual 2011

If you're mad about *Toy Story*, *Up*, *Monsters Inc.*, *Finding Nemo* and *WALL·E*, then we've got tons of treats for you! Inside you'll find fun features, puzzles, quizzes, stories and activities, all about your favourite characters.

Have fun!

EGMONT

We bring stories to life

First published in Great Britain 2010
by Egmont UK Limited,
239 Kensington High Street, London W8 6SA

Group Art Editor: Jeanette Ryall • Group Editor: Keilly Swift
• Designers: Clare Marshall, Anni Nolan • Writer: Olivia McLearon

© 2010 Disney Enterprises, Inc.
Slinky® Dog is a registered trademark of Poof-Slinky, Inc. © Poof-Slinky, Inc. Mr Potato Head® is a registered trademark of Hasbro, Inc. Used with permission © Hasbro, Inc. All rights reserved.

ISBN 978 1 4052 5246 1
1 3 5 7 9 10 8 6 4 2
Printed in Italy

All rights reserved. No part of this publication may be reproduced, stored in a retrieval system, or transmitted in any form or by any means, electronic, mechanical, photocopying, recording or otherwise, without the prior permission of the publisher and copyright owner.

Note to parents: adult supervision is recommended when sharp-pointed items, such as scissors, are in use.

Best Bits

Toy Story 3 is full of more fun with your favourite characters.

1 What next?

Andy is going to college, so the toys are in a panic. But as long as they stick together, they'll be OK ... won't they?

2 Arrival day

After being thrown out by mistake, the toys have no idea where they'll go. But Sunnyside Daycare looks like a nice place. Or so they think.

8

3 Lotso's crew

There's a new gang of toys in town! Their leader is Lotso, a cuddly, pink teddy bear. But beware! This bear has got bite and he's definitely the one in charge at Sunnyside Daycare!

4 A new Buzz

When the gang tries to escape from Sunnyside, Buzz's settings are accidentally switched – and he starts speaking Spanish! What will this mean for Buzz and his pals?

Meet new character, **Lotso!**

Which was your favourite part?

....

....

9

Alien Puzzlers

Can you help the Aliens with these tricky teasers?

Shadow Toys

See if you can match the shadows to the toys.

a

b

c

d

1

2

3

4

Animal Magic

Part of Hamm has magically disappeared! Work out which part it is from the pieces below.

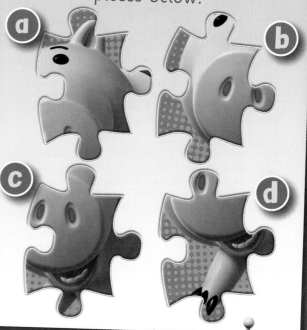

a

b

c

d

Find the Friends

Can you fit all of the gang's names into this crossword? We've filled in a few letters for you as clues.

N S E

N

B Y

D

Y

WOODY   SLINKY DOG
BUZZ   BULLSEYE
JESSIE   ALIENS
HAMM   REX

Answers:
Shadow
Toys: 1 = d,
2 = c, 3 = a,
4 = b

Animal
Magic: c

[crossword solution grid:
HAMM
JESSIE
REX
SLINKY
BULLSEYE
WOODY]

11

TV Toys

1. One day, the toys were all quietly playing in the bedroom. "Hey, Buzz, I'm bored, I think I'll go and watch TV on the bed instead," said Woody.

2. So he climbed up onto Andy's bed, and started flicking through the channels, using the remote control. "I need some excitement!" he giggled.

CRASH!

THWACK!

3. Suddenly, there was a commotion down on the floor. RC, the racing car, had zoomed across the bedroom and only just missed Buzz!

4. Next, a robot stomped through the toy soldiers' parade! "Try to keep it quiet, guys!" called Woody, as he carried on searching through the channels.

5. Just then, Woody found an old Western on one of the channels. He forgot all about the robot and turned the sound up so he could hear it above the noise.

6. Strange things were still happening down on the floor. But when Woody heard the fire engine siren blaring, he just turned the volume up some more.

7. The fire engine's siren got even louder! The robot and the racing car were still wildly whizzing around the room! Buzz decided to go and speak to Woody.

8. "I guess I'm not going to get to watch TV, after all," sighed Woody, after Buzz complained to him. He pressed the OFF button on the remote control.

13

9. Instantly, all of the crazy toys stopped. Buzz pressed the ON button on the remote control and the toys went wild again! "They're tuned into the same frequency as the TV!" gasped Buzz. So Woody and Buzz pressed more buttons. "This is much more fun than watching TV!" they laughed.

The end

Who's on TV?

Follow the lines on this dot-to-dot and find out who's on Woody's TV!

On the Run

The toys have broken out!
Help them on their way by brightening
them up with your colouring pens.

Toy Twist

Jessie is in a bit of a tangle!
Which rope will lead her
to Woody?

a

b

c

Well
done!

Answer: c

Odd One Out

Rex needs your help!

Can you help him find the odd one out in each row?

a

b

c

Answers: a) The third Alien only has two eyes, b) the second Lotso is blue, c) the third Hamm has just one ear.

17

Blast Off

Now you can join Buzz on his adventures in space, by making this amazing rocket!

I'm Buzz Lightyear. I come in peace.

SPACE RANGER LIGHTYEAR

LASER

You will need:

- A plastic bottle
- Silver foil
- Green and yellow card
- Black marker pen
- Orange felt tip
- Safety scissors
- Glue
- A paper cup

1

Wrap some silver foil around your plastic bottle. Cover the whole bottle, including the top.

2

Cut out two triangular shapes from the green card. Fold each one in half and put plenty of glue on one half of each triangle.

3

3

Stick the green triangles to the sides of the bottle. Cover the paper cup in silver foil and glue the bottom of the cup on to the bottom of the bottle.

4

Cut out two fire shapes from the yellow card and colour them in with an orange felt tip. Then stick them inside the paper cup. Now you're ready for blast off!

Top tip

Finish off your rocket with a window and a number!

Happy Anniversary!

Key

Use our key to fill in the missing words. Shout the names out whenever there's a picture!

Woody

Jessie

Buzz

Hamm

 woke up feeling really happy. Today w

the anniversary of the day he became Andy's.

He couldn't wait to see what

and his other friends had in store for him.

Andy was away, so they could play in his

bedroom all day long. "Morning,  ,"

 shouted from his shelf. "How

strange," thought  , "he hasn't

said happy anniversary."

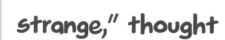

20

"Hey, , how are you today?"

beamed. But she didn't say happy anniversary

either. A few hours passed and still no one had

said happy anniversary! "You're quiet today, ,"

said .  was just about to say

something, when all of the toys started singing

happy anniversary to him! "But I thought you'd

forgotten," said. "We wanted to surprise

you,"  laughed. "Well, you certainly did

that,"  giggled.   **The end**

Who Said What?

The *Toy Story 3* characters have got their words mixed up!

Write the number or words next to the right toy.

1 "We've got a keeper!"

Clue:

2 "Glad to meetcha!"

Clue:

3 "Holy moly, guacamole!"

Clue:

4 "Silence, minions of Zurg!"

Clue:

5 "You've got a date with justice!"

Clue:

6 "Play! Real play! I can't wait!"

Clue:

23

Answers: 1) Lotso, 2) Jessie, 3) Hamm, 4) Buzz, 5) Woody, 6) Rex.

Where's Woody?

Can you spot Woody and the rest of the gang in this picture?

1 How many building blocks are there on the page?

2 What instrument is behind Buzz?

3 How many books are there on the page?

4 Can you spot Slinky Dog?

5 Where are the green army men?

6 Colour in Andy's ball below!

Where's your favourite hiding place? Shh, don't tell anyone!

Can you spot these toys in the picture? Tick them off once you've spotted them.

Answers: 1) Seven, 2) a tambourine, 3) six 4) he is in front of the building blocks, 5) in front of the bed.

Star Dash

Hamm needs to get to Mr Potato Head.

Help him by counting the number of stars along the way.

There are 4 stars.

Answer: 14

Friend Search

The names of Woody and Lotso's friends are hidden in this wordsearch.

```
E U Z S T R E T C H H
Z O D J K I C H U N K
B E H G A D E H W F G
U L A I R C Q S J Q H
Z N M W Z A B L C M Q
Z S M S Y O I I Q Y T
C G R P C Y G N R K W
N R D A Y K B K H N I
R Y L R E X A Y V G T
R S Y K B F B D E U C
N R P S K O Y O P C H
J E S S I E P G E A X
```

Cross off each name when you find it in the grid.

BUZZ	BIG BABY
JESSIE	CHUNK
HAMM	TWITCH
REX	SPARKS
SLINKY DOG	STRETCH

Answer:

27

Story Time

So you think you know all about Toy Story?
Test yourself with the ultimate Toy Story quiz!

1

Who replaces Woody as Andy's favourite toy in the first Toy Story film?

a Mr Potato Head
b Buzz Lightyear
c Big Baby

2

What does Andy get for Christmas in the first Toy Story film?

a Lotso
b A kitten
c A puppy

3

Which character yodels when they're excited?

a Jessie
b Slinky Dog
c Bullseye

4

Which of these toys does Woody save in Toy Story 2?

a Bullseye
b Rex
c Wheezy

5

Where is Andy about to
go in *Toy Story 3*?

a England
b A new house
c College

6

Whose catchphrase
is this? "To infinity
. . . and beyond!"

a Buzz Lightyear
b Hamm
c Woody

7

What's the name
of the nursery in
Toy Story 3?

a Sunshine Daycentre
b Sunnyside Daycare
c Sunnyside Up

8

Which of these toys
isn't a member of
Lotso's crew?

a Mr Potato Head
b Big Baby
c Stretch

Answers: 1) b, 2) c, 3) a, 4) c, 5) c, 6) a, 7) b, 8) a.

29

Fun and Games

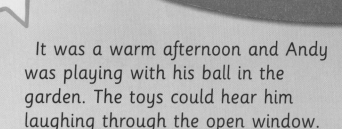

The toys want to play outside but Woody has an even better idea ...

It was a warm afternoon and Andy was playing with his ball in the garden. The toys could hear him laughing through the open window.

"He's having so much fun," said Hamm. "I really wish we could go outside too."

"We can't," said Woody sternly. "It's dangerous for toys on their own."

"Woody's right," agreed Slinky, "although, I would love to run across the grass like Andy."

"And I'd like to play ball," said Rex, gazing longingly out of the window.

"We can't go outside unless Andy takes us, OK!" exclaimed Woody.

The toys moaned loudly. "But," Woody continued, "there's no reason why the outside can't come to us!"

The toys watched as Woody turned on Andy's bedside lamp and shone it on to the floor. "That's the sun," he said.

"We could use Andy's rug for the grass!" said Hamm, excitedly.

"And we could make a swing out of Jessie's lasso!" added Buzz.

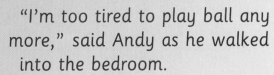

Soon the toys had gathered lots of outdoor props and had transformed Andy's room into a fun-filled garden.

They played catch, swung on the swing and played on the grass in the sunlight. They were having so much fun, they forgot all about Andy.

Suddenly they heard footsteps on the stairs.

"Andy's coming!" shouted Woody. "Clear up!"

The toys ran around, quickly putting everything back where it had come from.

"Get into your positions!" Woody ordered, as the door handle turned.

"I'm too tired to play ball any more," said Andy as he walked into the bedroom.

He picked up his toys and carried them downstairs and out into the garden. As he put them down on the grass, Woody grinned at Rex.

"Bringing the outside inside was fun," he whispered, "but actually being outside with Andy is even better!"

The end

Woody and Buzz

Bring this picture of Woody and Buzz to life.

Colour them in using your favourite pens.

Snap Shots

Look at these pictures.

Can you work out who each *Toy Story 3* character is?

oooooooooh!

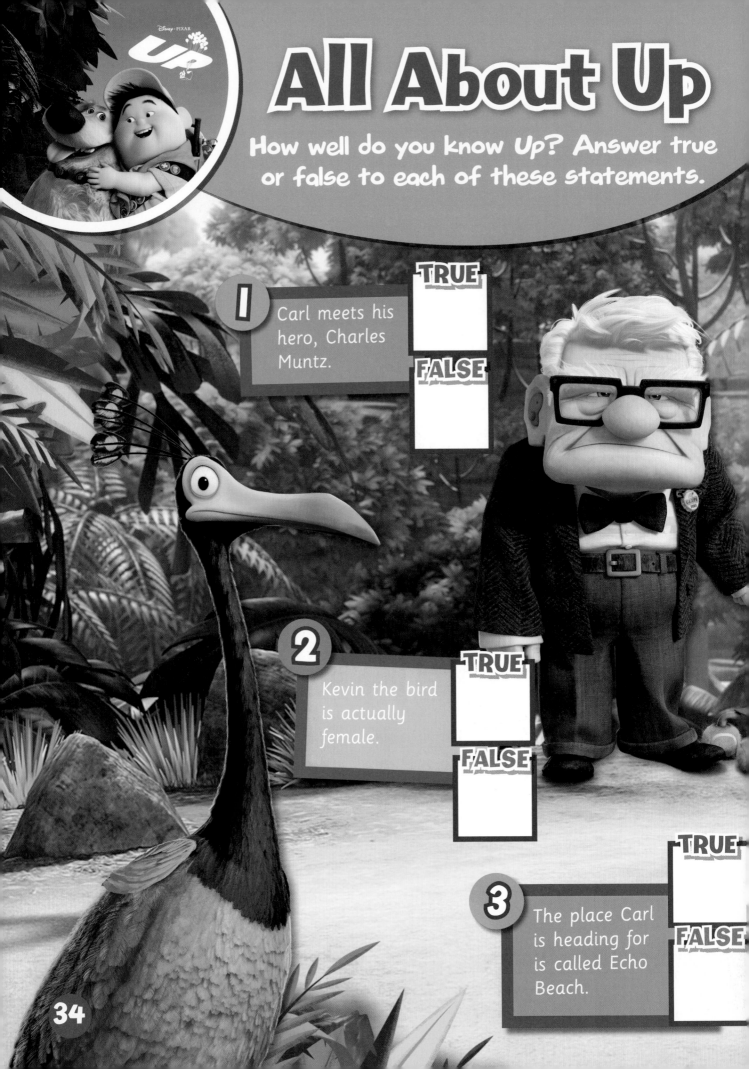

All About Up

How well do you know *Up*? Answer true or false to each of these statements.

1 Carl meets his hero, Charles Muntz.

TRUE

FALSE

2 Kevin the bird is actually female.

TRUE

FALSE

3 The place Carl is heading for is called Echo Beach.

TRUE

FALSE

34

How did you do?

1-2 Oh no! It's time for you to watch *Up* again!

3-4 Pretty good. You're nearly "up" there with the experts!

5-6 Wow! You're a total *Up* ace!

4

Russell is a Forest Forager!

TRUE

FALSE

5

A dog called Dug joins Carl, Russell and Kevin on their adventure.

TRUE

FALSE

6

Russell wants to earn his Assisting the Elderly badge.

TRUE

FALSE

Answers: 1) True, 2) True, 3) False – he's heading for Paradise Falls, 4) False – he's a Wilderness Explorer, 5) True, 6) True.

Best Buddies

Carl and Russell are the best of friends.

Can you find five differences between these two pictures of them?

Colour a paw print when you find a difference.

Answers: In picture b – Russell has a red star on his flag, his neck tie is green, Carl has lost his badge, Carl's bow tie has polka dots, there is a tennis ball missing from his walking stick.

Colourful Kevin

Grab your felt tips and colour in this picture of Kevin.

Make her as bright as you like!

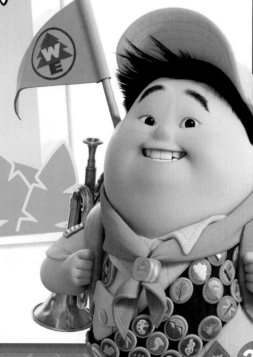

Kevin's feathers are bright and beautiful! Which colours will you use?

Dug's Special Surprise

Key

Use the key to fill in the missing words, that have been replaced by pictures!

Russell

Wilderness Explorers

Carl

Dug

 was very excited! The were

going to have a picnic and was making

an ice cream sundae! He found and

 and told them about the picnic. "That's

great,"  said. "I'd love to help you

make it!" The next day, they started making

the ice cream sundae. They were having so

much fun, that they didn't notice a rather sad

looking in the corner. "Hey, ,

are you OK?"  asked. "I am sad

because I cannot help you make an ice cream

sundae, and I cannot eat it either," replied  .

The friends felt really bad. "What can we do?"

asked. "I'm not sure," replied sadly.

Suddenly, had an idea. "After we've finished

making the ice cream sundae, let's make a

sundae!" "What a fantastic idea!" grinned.

They finished the ice cream sundae and then started

making the  sundae. It was made from all of

his favourite foods. "Thank you so much, you have

made me very happy!" said  .

Up, Up and Away

Grab some friends for this fantastically fun game!
Who will be the first to do all of the challenges
on the balloons and go up, up and away?

1 Do an impression of Dug!

2 Answer this – What does Kevin love eating?

3 Draw a badge for Russell!

4 Answer this – What type of animals work for Muntz?

5 Answer this – Who does this house belong to?

6 Answer this – Name three of the dogs in Up.

Player 1
Russell

40

How to play

- You need a dice and two players.
- Both pages have the same challenges, but one player follows Carl's challenges and the other player follows Russell's.
- Take it in turns to throw the dice and then do the challenge on the balloon with the same number as the dice.
- Colour in the number on the balloon once you've completed the challenge. The first to complete all six is the winner!

1 Do an impression of Dug!

2 Answer this – What does Kevin love eating?

3 Draw a badge for Russell!

4 Answer this – What type of animals work for Muntz?

5 Answer this – Who does this house belong to?

6 Answer this – Name three of the dogs in *Up*.

Player 2
Carl

41

Answers: 2) chocolate, **4)** dogs, **5)** Carl, **6)** choose from Alpha, Beta, Gamma and Dug.

My Own Adventure

It's time to start planning your own adventure!
Fill in the page below and you could be an
explorer, just like Russell!

Where would you go?

Carl and Ellie dreamt of
going to Paradise Falls,
but where would you go
on your adventure?

....

Write your answer here.

Your badge

Russell wanted to get his,
"Assisting the Elderly" badge.
What kind of badge would
you like to earn?

Your friends

Russell went on his
adventure with Carl.
Which friends would you
take on your adventure?

Write your friends' names here.

Make your own binoculars!

You will need:

- a ruler
- 1 kitchen roll tube
- Green paper
- Felt tip pens
- Safety scissors
- Glue
- Sharp pencil
- Ribbon
- Sticky tape

Every explorer needs a pair of binoculars. Follow our step-by-step guide to making your own pair.

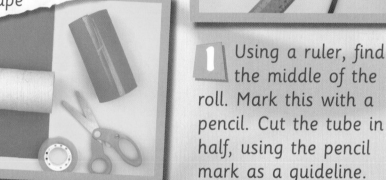

1 Using a ruler, find the middle of the roll. Mark this with a pencil. Cut the tube in half, using the pencil mark as a guideline.

2 Roll the green paper over each half and tape in place. Stick the two parts side by side, with some tape across the bottom and the top.

3 Ask an adult to make two holes near the top of your binoculars. Tie one end of the ribbon through each hole to make a neck strap. Then decorate with felt tips.

Up Puzzlers

Can you help Dug and Russell work out the answers to these brain-straining puzzles?

Which Muntz?

Which picture of Muntz is the odd one out?

a b c d

A-maze-ing!

Start

Carl needs to get throug[h] the maze and rescu[e] Kevin! See if you ca[n] help him

Finish

Weird Words

Russell's confused! Can you help him fill in the missing letters in Alpha's message to Dug and work out what he's saying?

"Y_u m_st _ear th_ con_ of s_ame."

The missing letters are:
e, u, o, e, h and w

Sizing It Up . . .

Can you put these pictures of Alpha in order of size, starting with the tallest?

 a

 b

 c

 d

tallest ↑

shortest ↓

Answers: Which Muntz: Picture b – his moustache is missing, A-maze-ing!; Weird Words: "You must wear the cone of shame." Sizing It Up: d, b, c, a.

WALL·E

Welcome to

It's hundreds of years in the future and planet Earth is covered in rubbish. The only being who lives on Earth is a robot called **WALL·E** ...

WALL·E

WALL·E's name stands for Waste Allocation Load Lifter Earth-Class. He's a lonely robot with a big heart who spends his days collecting rubbish. His life changes when a female probe-bot named EVE lands on Earth – a new friend for WALL·E!

WALL·E has a plant which he loves. Draw a plant for WALL·E here.

WALL·E

EVE

Probe-bot EVE, Extraterrestrial Vegetation Evaluator, has been sent to Earth from space to find out if there is any life there. She becomes friends with WALL·E and together they manage to save planet Earth!

Question:
What colour are EVE's eyes?

M-O

M-O, a microbe obliterator, loves cleaning! When he first meets WALL·E, he can't stop cleaning him. M-O and EVE help save WALL·E's life.

47

Tangled Up

WALL·E's got EVE in a real twist! Can you spot five differences between these two pictures?

a

b

Tick a box when you spot a difference.

Follow the rocket's path with your finger!

Answers: In picture b – 1) EVE has yellow eyes, 2) a string of fairy lights is missing, 3) the plug on the end of the lights is missing, 4) WALL·E's right track has gone, 5) part of his hand has disappeared.

Grow Your Own

WALL·E found a plant when he was cleaning planet Earth. Now you can grow your own plant by following these instructions.

You will need:
- An egg
- cress seeds
- cotton wool
- a clean yogurt pot or egg cup

1 Ask an adult to help you boil an egg for breakfast. Eat it carefully, as you will need to keep the shell.

2 Fill the shell with damp cotton wool and sprinkle some cress seeds on top. Now pop the shell in a clean yogurt pot or an egg cup.

Colour in WALL·E's plant pot.

3 Water it a little bit every day and watch as your cress grows. WALL·E would be proud!

Fishing Fun

1. WALL·E loved looking through old things. One day he found a book about fishing. It made him think that fishing looked like it was really fun!

2. WALL·E didn't have a fishing rod, so he cleverly made one from a pipe, some string and a coat hook, with a magnet at the end of the line.

3. WALL·E then found a good spot at the river to fish. He cast his fishing line in, hoping that he'd catch a really big fish.

4. But the book hadn't mentioned that a river needs to have water in it! WALL·E whistled to himself as he waited for a big fish to swim by.

Ahhhhh!

5. Suddenly, something tugged at WALL·E's fishing line. Had he caught a fish? He reeled his line upwards, but it was a broken bicycle!

6. WALL·E didn't mind though. He carried on fishing and caught a teddy bear, a boot, a trumpet and a radio. WALL·E was a great fisherman!

BEEEEP!

The end

7. WALL·E beeped in excitement as e reeled in yet another new object. was long and red. Could this be kind of fish, he wondered?

8. Just then, there was a sudden gust of wind and the object popped open. The fish was an umbrella! Fishing really was lots of fun!

Robot Race

Join WALL·E, EVE and M-O as they race around
the Axiom spaceship in this super-fun game!
Who will get to the finish first?

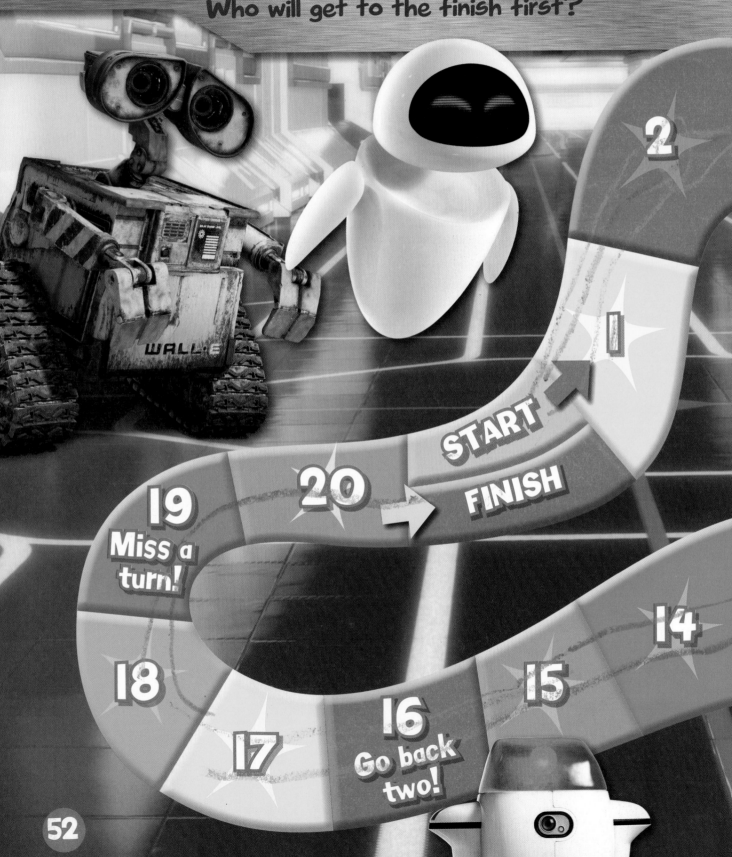

HOW TO PLAY

- You will need a dice and a counter for each player.
- This game is for up to three players. Decide who will be WALL·E, EVE and M-O.
- Take it in turns to throw the dice and move along the track, using the number on the dice as the guide.
- Follow the instructions along the way.
- The first player to reach the finish is the winner!

3

4

5
Go forward one!

6

7
Miss a turn!

8

9

10
Go forward three!

11

12

13

True or False?

How well do you know *Finding Nemo?* Test yourself with these fun film facts!

1 Nemo and Marlin are puffer fish.

TRUE

FALSE

2 Sheldon is a seahorse.

TRUE

FALSE

3 Marlin and Dory are swallowed by a humpback whale.

TRUE

FALSE

54

How did you do?

0-2 Are you sure your name's not Dory? Better luck next time!

3-4 OK, but you could do better. You might want to re-watch the film and test yourself again!

5-6 Wow, Nemo expert! You'd certainly know what to do if Nemo ever got lost again!

4 The dentist's niece is called Darla.

TRUE

FALSE

5 Nemo is taken to Perth, Australia.

TRUE

FALSE

6 Crush and Squirt are twin brother sea turtles.

TRUE

FALSE

Answers: 1) false – they're clown fish, 2) true, 3) true, 4) true, 5) false – Nemo is taken to Sydney, Australia, 6) false – they're father and son sea turtles.

Help Nemo

Can you help Nemo solve these deep-sea puzzles?

Same Shoal!

Which two shoals are exactly the same?

1
2
3
4
5

Eye Eye

Can you work out who these eyes belong to?

56

Shell Sequence

Follow the sequence and work out the next letter in each pattern.

1) a a b a a ? — The next shell is ▢

2) a b c a b ? — The next shell is ▢

3) a b a b a ? — The next shell is ▢

Finding Names

Using the pictures as clues, fill in the crossword to spell out one of Crush's favourite words in the yellow boxes!

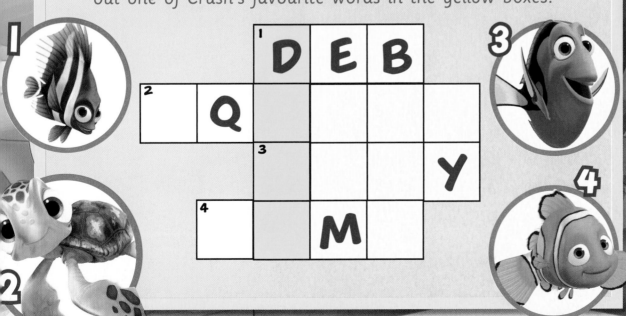

```
     1
     D  E  B
 2
    Q
        3
            Y
 4
        M
```

Answers: Same Shoal! 2 and 5. Eye: Dory. Shell Sequence: 1) b, 2) c, 3) b. Finding Names: 2) SQUIRT, 3) DORY, 4) NEMO. They spell out DUDE.

Lucky Escape

1. Pearl and Nemo were exploring the ocean one day and found a cave that they'd never seen before. "Let's take a closer look," Pearl said excitedly.

2. Pearl swam straight in without a second thought, but Nemo was worried. "Pearl, I don't think this is a cave!" he said, as he swam after her.

3. Then suddenly, the cave closed! "We're trapped!" Pearl cried. "Caves don't just close on their own," Nemo told her. "I think we're inside a whale!"

4. "I wish Dory was with us," Nemo sighed. "She can speak Whale, so she'd be able to get us out of here," he explained to Pearl.

5. "Ha ha, I can't believe she can speak Whale! Can you speak Whale, too?" Pearl giggled. Nemo smiled and said, "No, but I've just thought of something!"

6. "Let's make the whale laugh," Nemo suggested. "If we tickle him and make him laugh, he'll open his mouth again." So, the two friends started tickling him.

7. Seconds later, the whale started laughing. But instead of opening its mouth, the whale's laughter made water shoot out of its blowhole!

8. Nemo and Pearl had the ride of their lives as they were blasted into the air by the whale's water jet. They had escaped! "Wheeee!" they laughed together.

Rocking Pool

Nemo and his friends have found
a huge rock filled with fun.
Go on and explore it!

1 What has Nemo found?

2 How many seashells can you find?

3 How many fish are there on the page?

Answers: 1) An eel, 2) there are two seashells, 3) twelve — including Nemo and Marlin at the top and three in question 6, 4) six, 5) Pearl is next to the starfish in the corner and Sheldon is near the centre, 6) c.

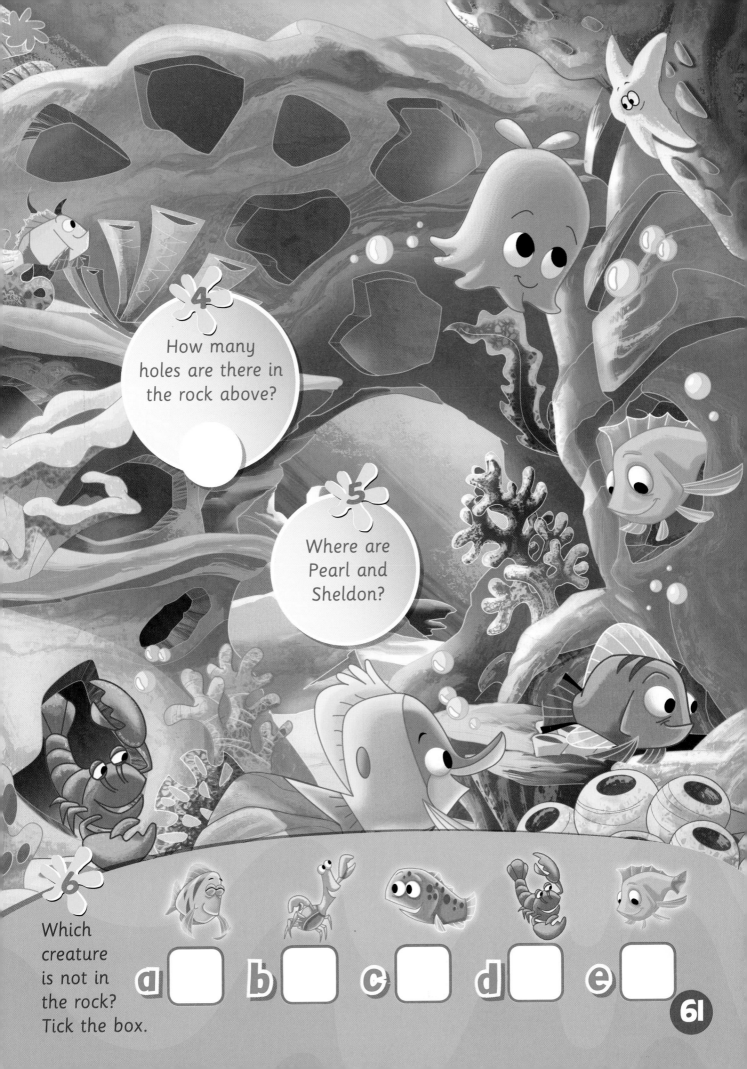

4 How many holes are there in the rock above?

5 Where are Pearl and Sheldon?

6 Which creature is not in the rock? Tick the box.

a ☐ b ☐ c ☐ d ☐ e ☐

Brilliant Beasties

Match each of these Monsters, Inc. characters to the descriptions in the boxes.

Write the correct number in the star beside the character.

1 This monster is large and furry and the top scarer for Monsters, Inc.

2 He is Sulley's green best friend.

3 This monster has snakes instead of hair.

4 He is the big boss at the Monsters, Inc. factory.

5 This monster lives for paperwork! Her job is dispatch manager at the factory.

Roz

Celia

Mike

DISNEY·PIXAR
MONSTERS, INC.

Mr Waternoose

6 Sulley's rival, who's a master of disguise.

7 This little lady thinks that Sulley is a giant kitty at first!

Sulley

Randall

Boo

Answers: 1) Sulley, 2) Mike, 3) Celia, 4) Mr Waternoose, 5) Roz, 6) Randall, 7) Boo.

Through the Door

Randall is jealous of Sulley's top scare score and will do anything to try and beat it...

One day, Sulley happily walked out of a door, after another very good scare.

"Well done, Sulley, that's a full canister. You'll easily have the top scare score today!" chuckled best friend, Mike.

Randall was watching and felt very jealous of Sulley's success. "I'm much better than that big ball of blue fur. I should be getting the top scare score," said Randall.

He noticed Mike checking a list for the number of the next door to be brought to Sulley's scare station.

"Sulley gets the top scores because he gets the best doors!" hissed Randall.

So, Randall crept up behind Mike and peeked at the list of doors. The one at the bottom of the list had a red circle around it.

"Why is that door circled? I bet there are extra screams in that bedroom!" said Randall.

Mike jumped with shock. "That's none of your business!" he replied.

Randall frowned. He was sure there was something special about that door. "If I had that door, I'd get the top scare score," he thought.

It was lunchtime and everyone was getting ready to leave the scare floor. Randall quickly made himself invisible and watched Mike put the list down by Sulley's scare station.

When Mike and Sulley were gone, Randall crept over to the list and read the number that was circled. "Hmm, door 456. That's going to be my lucky number!" he laughed.

Randall rushed to his own scare station and keyed 456 into the control panel. The door silently arrived and Randall turned the handle and stepped inside.

When lunch was over, everyone noticed the door at Randall's station. "Oh dear! Randall has gone through door 456!" gasped Sulley.

Suddenly, the door burst open and Randall fell out. He was covered in children's clothes and toys. "That's the messiest room ever!" he cried.

"That's why I circled it, to warn Sulley to be extra careful!" giggled Mike, as the Child Detection Agency suddenly appeared.

Mike, Sulley and the other monsters watched as the C.D.A. began the cleaning process on an unhappy Randall!

The end

Grrrrrr!

Mike's Door Sign

Get Mike to welcome your favourite visitors, by making this fun, fuzzy door sign!

You will need:

- Green card
- Green felt
- White, green, black and cream funky foam
- A small saucepan lid
- Pencil
- Safety scissors
- Glue
- Black marker pen

1

Draw around the saucepan lid onto the green card and felt and cut them both out. Glue the circles together.

2

Draw Mike's eye, mouth, teeth and horns onto the funky foam and cut them out. Glue them to the felt side of the circle to make his face.

3

More monster makes ...

Monster Top Tip

Tape a loop of ribbon to Mike's back, then hang him on your bedroom door for total monster-cool!

Now draw Mike's arms and legs onto green foam and cut them out. Draw on details with a black marker, then glue them to his body!

1 This scary guy is made from colourful card. Make a bunch!

2 Googly-eyed pompom beasts are pretty cool and easy to make, too!

3 You'll need pipecleaners, and tin foil to make this crazy robot creature!

67

Monster Madness

Can you help the Monsters, Inc. gang solve this puzzle?

There are five differences in picture two. Tick a star each time you spot one.

Answer: Five Things: In picture 2 – Sulley is in the mirror, the balloon is green, the ball has nothing on it, Mike's eye is blue and the sun has disappeared.

ADVERTISEMENT

© 2010 Disney/Pixar